AS

THE

TWIG

IS

BENT

EX LIBRIS

THE BELANGERS

AS
THE
TWIG
IS
BENT

photographs by julie ann lyman   text by diane david

THE BOBBS-MERRILL COMPANY, INC. a subsidiary of Howard W. Sams & Co., Inc.

publishers · INDIANAPOLIS · KANSAS CITY · NEW YORK

"'Tis education forms the common mind;
Just as the twig is bent the tree's inclined."

ALEXANDER POPE: Moral Essays, 1 (Of the
Knowledge and Characters of Men), 1733

PREFACE

It is surprising to discover, from the title of this book, that one so contemporary as Julie Ann Lyman is acquainted with the writings of Alexander Pope—or perhaps that knowledge should be credited to Diane David, who is of a comparable age, or lack of age, to Miss Lyman. But it is a fitting association, too, since I am sure the Wasp of Twickenham would have viewed with approval this pictorial and textual attempt to interpret the shadowy-shining world of childhood.

I found this a worthwhile book not only because of the excellent photographs made by Miss Lyman during various assignments for *The Chicago Tribune,* and not only because Miss David's captions fit the mood of each picture as if tailor-made, but also because text and photos, viewed in sequence, establish a cumulative effect that is curiously powerful.

These are more than just "cute" photographs of some charming youngsters and the adults who make up a child's background. They are more than accusing portraits of kids whose chances for a decent break depend on how the obviously loaded dice spin to a stop. This is a related set of photos, which, together with the text, offer a commentary on existence as seen through the eyes of a normal child, a child who feels certain things about his surroundings, his parents, his playmates, yet is not articulate enough to express these feelings.

Miss Lyman and Miss David, then, are interpreters. They have translated the tongue-tied silences and the shy and insufficient words into a panorama which has the crystal ring of truth. There are joy and laughter in the book. There are sadness and tears. And there is humor. The diapered toddler in tennis shoes, "racing" past the ancient with his cane and the back-turned policeman (who may shortly be scouring the neighborhood to find her) is one of the most tenderly mirthful things I've seen.

Knowing Miss Lyman, I am certain that the appearance in her photographs of children of many races is no accident. But the spacing of their appearances, the seemingly artless way in which the scene changes from slum to seashore, from Caucasian to Negro to Oriental, gives added impact to the unspoken theme that children are children and deserving of the same chance for life, liberty, and at least a run for happiness no matter what their origins.

This book will annoy some who see it, for there are some Americans, anomalous as it sounds, who resent even pictorial equality. But they are in the minority and, I believe, a vanishing breed. Perhaps books like this, while not essentially propaganda for anything but childhood, will help speed that vanishing.

You might say *As the Twig Is Bent* is against poverty, prejudice, ignorance, ugliness, and cruelty, and is for beauty, justice, and all other things splendid and just, and perhaps unattainable.

Yet you can't really put your finger on how these effects are created. They depend on a face peering through a wire fence, the squalor of a slum, the way a mother looks at her baby, the hopelessness that is evident in a fully-clothed youngster curled up disconsolately in his bed because there is no other place to hide, a family at dinnertime, or a playground dappled with sunlight filtered through the leaves.

This is an indirect book—one which will mean different things to different persons, all of them good things. It is a book I am glad was put together and published, a book Julie Ann Lyman and Diane David may be proud to have co-authored. It is a book to make you realize, if you've forgotten, that childhood is not all dolls and marbles and hoops and ice-cream cones (if kids still play with hoops). It is a simple book, one that makes you think, and I wish it a long and prosperous life and many, many printings.

ROBERT CROMIE

AS

THE

TWIG

IS

BENT

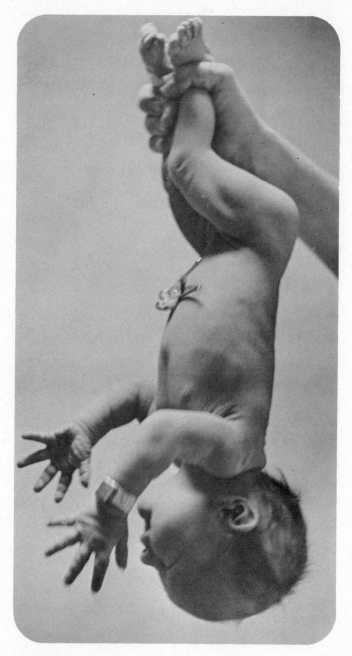

Who am I?
What's my name?
I don't know yet.
But I am here; a
part of Earth, a part
of God, a part of You.

It's so big out there.
Sounds and smells, lights
and shadows, everything
moves around me .

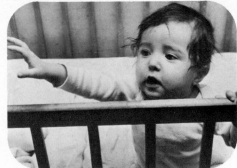

I want to touch it.

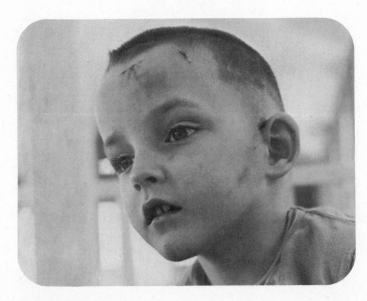

But it slips through
my fingers like the sun.

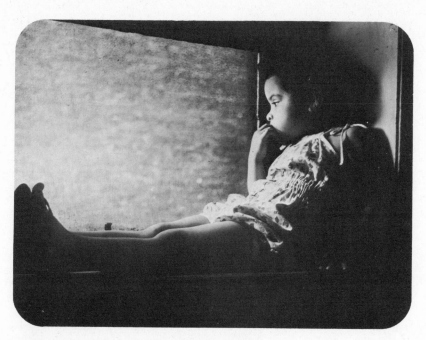

I am growing up, they say.
But I wonder what they mean.

No one can tell me how high
is up. Does everyone grow there?

Today I learned to walk!

Now I can go everywhere and
see everything . . . and *touch* everything!

But They won't let me.

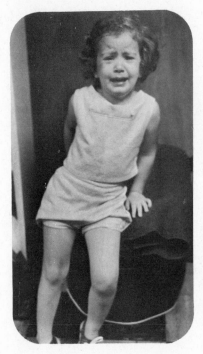
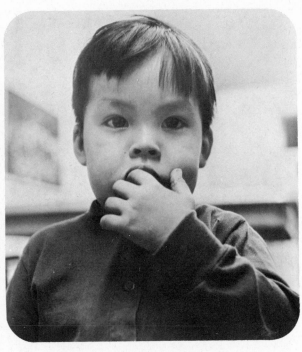

Why won't they understand?   I didn't mean any harm.

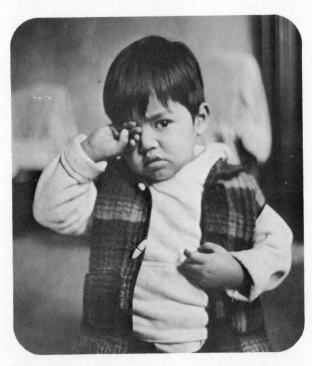

I just wanted to feel what it felt like.

I think I'll go off by myself,

and find someone to play with,

someone who won't tell me what to do . . .

someone who wants to
know what's *inside*,
just because . . .

someone I can tell
a *secret* to . . .

because I know he won't tell
anyone else.

Everything is so much fun! Sometimes
I just want to turn the world upside down . . .

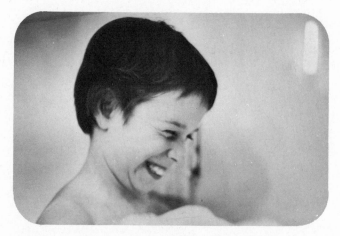

because I'm happy,
because the bubbles tickle my nose,

because I can *do* things by myself,

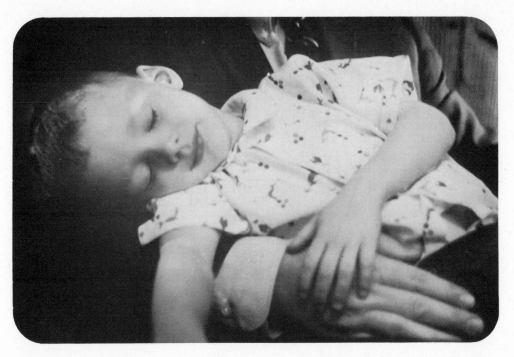

because Someone takes care of me,

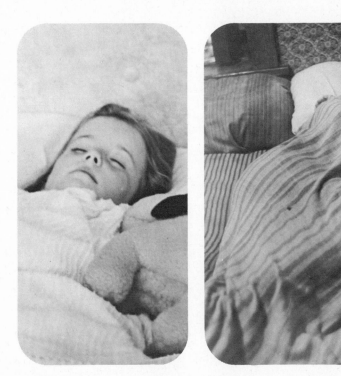

and I feel warm and wanted.

and Someone watches over me,
although I really don't know
who He is . . .

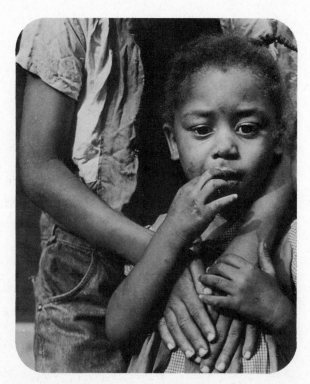

but sometimes I wonder if He really
does watch over *everyone.*

I think about things like that a lot.

But so many things
seem to be
so much bigger than I am.

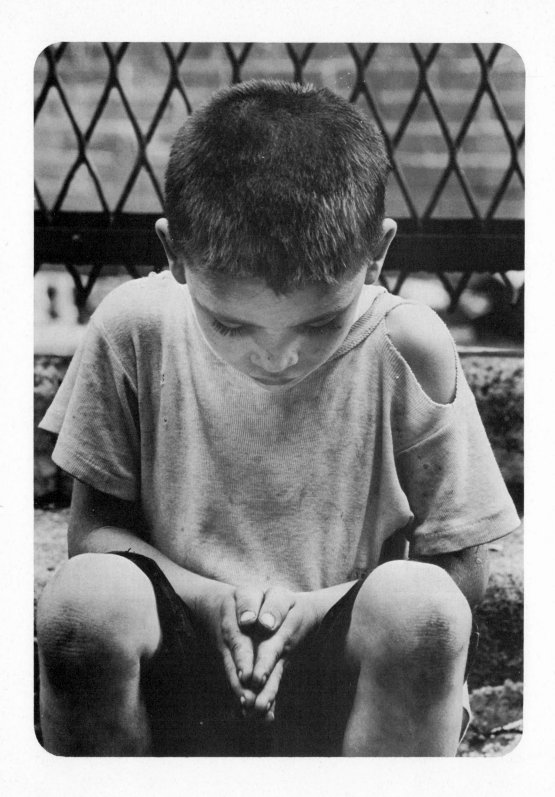

Maybe when I really grow up, I'll understand.

Pretty soon,
I guess I'll have to go to school.

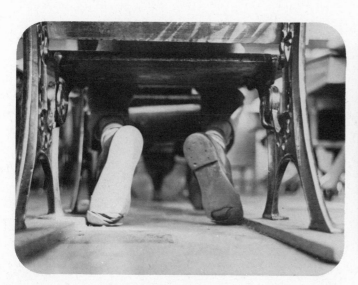

What if the other kids don't like me?

sometimes the kids can
be awfully mean . . .

just like grown-ups.

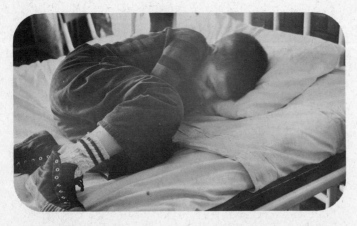

but who cares. I've got more important
things to do, anyway.

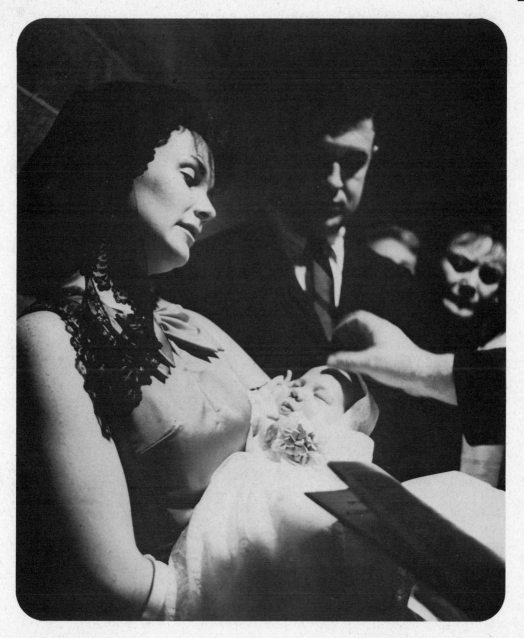

2

Does it begin with hands?
I do not know;
but out of that frightening rush
of sights and sounds
smiles and voices,
they come to claim me . . .

and I am not alone.

they are bigger than the whole world,

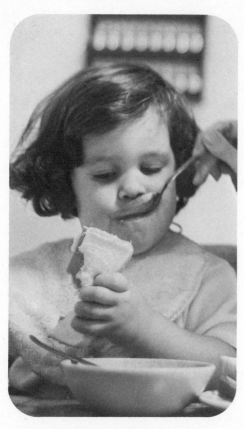

and much stronger, too!

they help me to reach up

and hold me back from
reaching too far.

My mother's hands
can do everything.

I wonder how
they can know so much
about so many things.

My father's hands are
strong and wise and sure.

They can fix anything in the world.

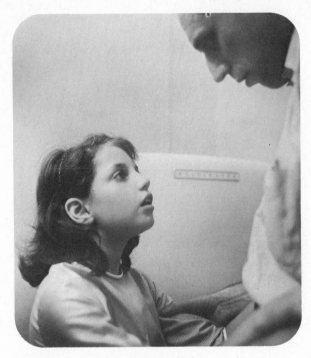

but they're never too busy
to stop

and listen

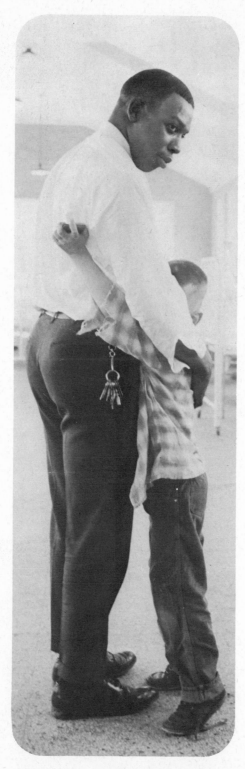

when it's really important.

They're never too busy
to explain what is
a hippopotamus,

or how a rocket
can land on the moon,

or to blow up a balloon

or to show how,

or why . . .

or to share a secret,
just between us.

My mother's hands are beautiful.

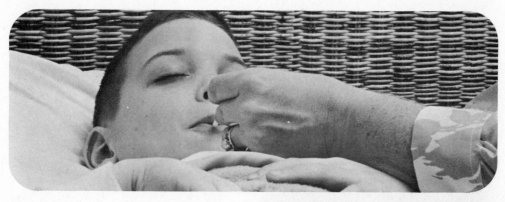

They're softer than
anyone else's .

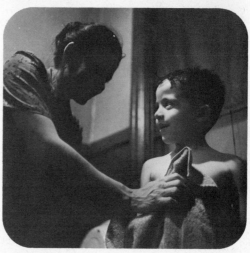

And even when they do those mysterious things
I don't completely understand . . .

I know they're part
of a world I shall
one day inherit . . .

just as I know
they will one day
let me go.

28

3

Parents are funny people.

Sometimes they're kind of hard to understand.

They either laugh

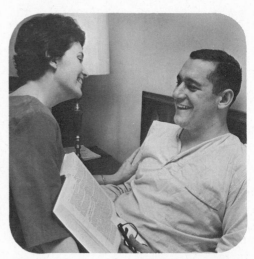

at the silliest things

and tease each other just like kids,

or they get very serious

and plan for something called the future.

I think my favorite time in the whole world
is when my daddy
comes home.

I think Mom feels that way too .

Dinner is the most fun 'cause then we all get to be together.

Most of the time Mom's busy in the kitchen,

and Dad's reading

or in his study.

But Sunday we have him all to ourselves,

and we can play ball

or go shopping

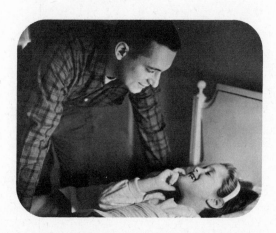

or just talk things over.

Mothers are a lot of fun
when they aren't telling you
what to do,

and once in a while
they can even help
with your homework.

Grandmothers are warm
and soft and great
to have around.

Sisters and brothers can be
all right sometimes,

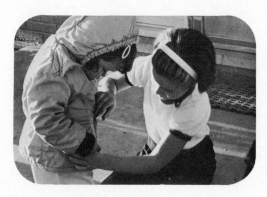

but sometimes they're
an awful nuisance

and they just get in the way.

Sometimes I see my parents
look at each other in
a special kind of way
and I feel
left out . . .

but most of the time it's swell

just being a family together.

4

My house is a big house,

and there are many trees around it.

We live on such
a quiet street
that sometimes it seems
as though no one
really lives there
at all.

Sometimes it's a lonely street,   especially at night
when I look out of my window

and see so many things I do not understand.

My city is a great stone cavern.

Its walls reach up to the sky,

its streets speak
in strange languages,

and they sparkle at night
like the stars.

There are always so many faces.

Where are they all going?

Don't they ever get lost . . .
or afraid?

My house
isn't very big inside;

sometimes
it's kind of crowded,

there isn't very much room
to play

inside or out.

I guess some people have
prettier houses,

and more fun.

But I have a room
all to myself . . .

I guess that's more
than some kids have.

They tell me to be grateful
for the roof over my head .

What do they mean by grateful?

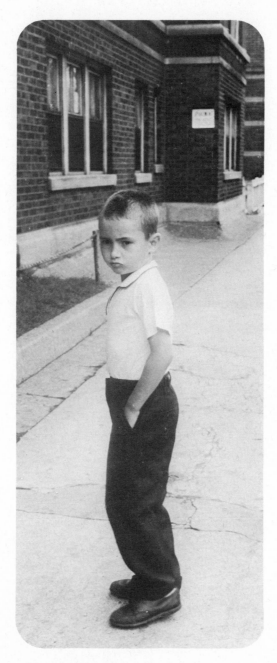

5

I remember how much
I didn't want
to go to school that first day.

There were so many things
I had to do outside.
And besides,
they make you sit up straight,

and say all those funny words
with your hand on your heart,

After a while it got to be
kind of fun, like drawing,

and pay attention all the time.

or milk and cookies in the morning.

I still wasn't convinced
that I was going to stay,
but it was getting better.

Until suddenly
I was supposed to learn how
to make words out of
all those silly letters
my mother taught me.

I didn't know what
the teacher was talking about.

Words were
something you said . . .

how could you tell which·
letters to put together?

How could a letter sound like
one thing
one time
and something else,
another time?

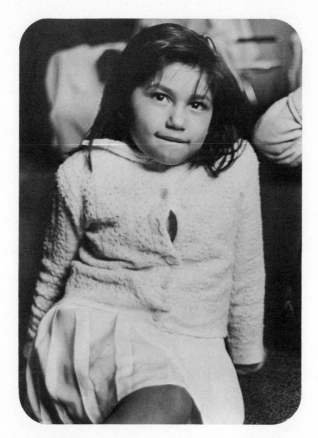

Of course,
if the words always looked
exactly the same way . . .

Then, one day, I got it!

I could read!

Of course,
I still made mistakes then . . .

but that seems
like a long time ago.

Now there's so much to learn,

and so much to do.

There's so much to understand

about the world

and why it is the
way it is;

about the faith of my father,

the language of my people,

the history of my creed,

and about myself . . .

Who I am,

and what I shall someday become.

I guess maybe school isn't so bad after all . . .

even when you get into trouble with the teacher . . .

or get sent down to the principal's office,

or get so sleepy
you can hardly keep your eyes open.

Then somehow,
like magic,
it's summer again.

6

Grown-ups have the most fun.

They can do anything
they feel like,

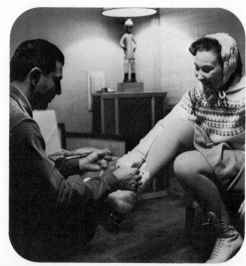

and nobody
ever tells them
what to do.

Grown-ups get
to stay up late
and have parties,

and drive around in big, shiny cars,

and make all the mess they want.

They can climb almost up to the sky,

or ride around it in funny looking machines.

They can wear pretty hats
and go to luncheons,

or work outside on a boat,

or inside a great huge office
with lots of other people.

Grown-ups
are never
afraid.

They can pilot helicopters,

and make as much noise as they want.

Grown-ups get to work
in stores with all kinds
of good things to eat,

and go shopping
whenever they feel like it,

and work on cars
and actually
get money for it.

Grown-ups are smart, too.
They get to be executives
and go to meetings
and everybody has to listen to them.

I think very seriously
about what I'm going to be
when I'm grown up.

Maybe I'll be very rich
and have lots of pretty clothes
and go to balls,

or be a secretary,

or a nurse,
and discuss things
like life and death.

When I grow up   or a policeman,
I'll be tall
and strong . . .

maybe I'll be a
star basketball player,

or an artist,

or maybe I'll drive an express train from coast to coast,

or play with a jazz group,

or be president of something,
and smoke big, black cigars
and tell everyone what to do.

But sometimes I wonder
why grown-ups look so serious.

And why
they say
they're always tired . . .

and why they sometimes seem
so far away,

even when you're right
next to them . . .

maybe they're
afraid of growing up.

Maybe growing up
isn't so much fun, after all.

7

I never get tired of playing,
'cause there's almost always
something to do . . .

something important,

like hitting
the winning run

or bringing it in

because
your folks are watching you . . .

or cooking up a big surprise,

or just
going down to watch
the express come through.

Sometimes
I just feel like running
to the end of the world

and diving in

and floating on my back
for a hundred years.

But sometimes I don't feel like anything at all,

and I just want to be by myself. Of course, you can
get into a lot of trouble that way.

Sometimes grown-ups
just don't understand,

and other times they can
really be
kind of swell . . .

I wish things
could stay the way they are,
forever.

8

I think a lot about God
when I'm alone.

Does He really
live in
all those houses?

Does He really listen

when I talk to Him?

Can He really tell
what I'm thinking?

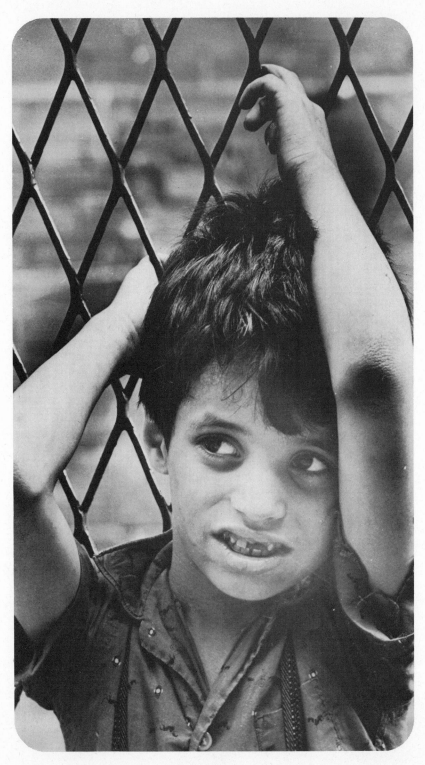

Or how I feel?

I used to think
He looked like an old man
with a white beard
I once saw . . .

or was someone strong
and smart
like my big brother.

But I learned He isn't like that at all.

He's very, very old,

and He has many faces,

and many,

many servants,

and He speaks

in many languages.

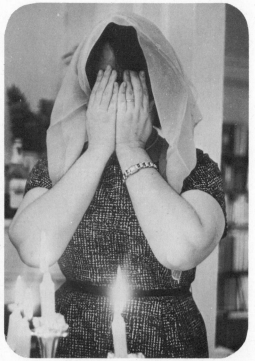

And He lives in our house, too.

Sometimes I think
I'm a little afraid
of Him.

9

They tell us the world has millions and millions of people
living on it;
and that there are millions and
millions of worlds
in the Universe.

I sure wish I could understand what
the teacher means by Universe.

But I'm gonna go there someday.

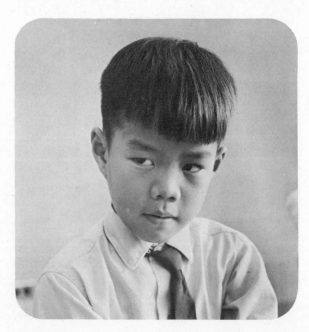

They tell us anybody can grow up
to be president.

all you have to do is
study real hard,

and be a good person,

and listen,

and watch,

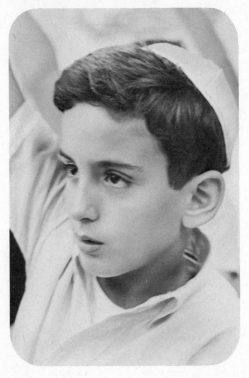

And learn.

But do they
really mean anybody?

I'll bet they don't.

I never heard of a lady president.

Of course,
there were all those Queens . . . .

If I got to be Queen
I'd give everyone candy twice a day,
and behead anyone
who wanted to start a war.

And nobody would talk mean to
anyone else.

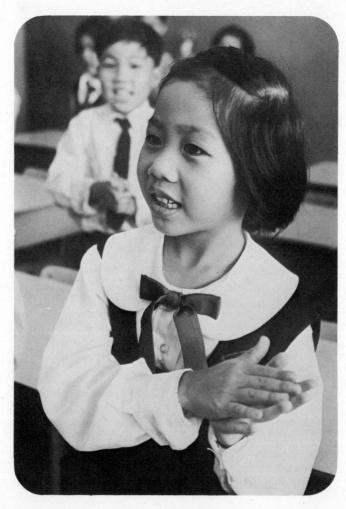

Because everyone would speak
the same language.